M000168979

TRANQUIL TREES

ARTIST'S COLORING BOOK

PETER PAUPER PRESS, INC.
White Plains, NY

PETER PAUPER PRESS
Fine Books and Gifts Since 1928

OUR STORY

In 1928, at the age of twenty-two, Peter Beilenson began printing books on a small press in the basement of his parents' home in Larchmont, New York. Peter—and later, his wife, Edna—sought to create fine books that sold at "prices even a pauper could afford."

Today, still family owned and operated, Peter Pauper Press continues to honor our founders' legacy—and our customers' expectations—of beauty, quality, and value.

Used under license from Bigstock.com: Images on pages 5, 7, 17, 19, 25, 43, 47, and 49.

All other images used under license from Shutterstock.com.

Designed by Tesslyn Pandarakalam

Copyright © 2016
Peter Pauper Press, Inc.
202 Mamaroneck Avenue
White Plains, NY 10601
All rights reserved
ISBN 978-1-4413-2188-6
Printed in China
7 6 5 4 3 2 1

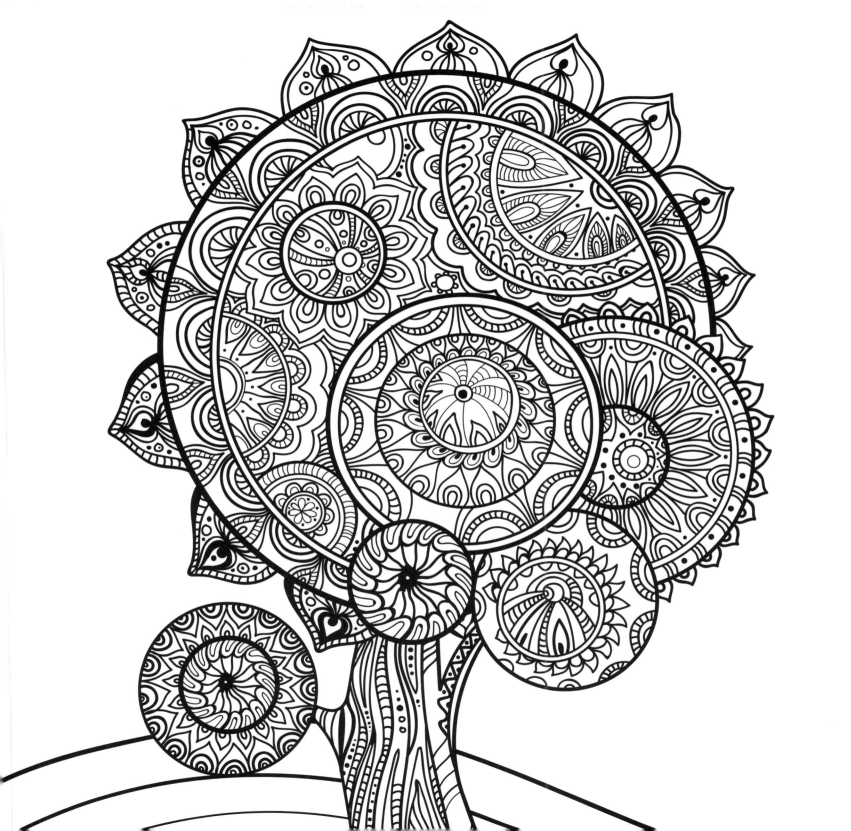